MANUAL HANDLING

in the

health services

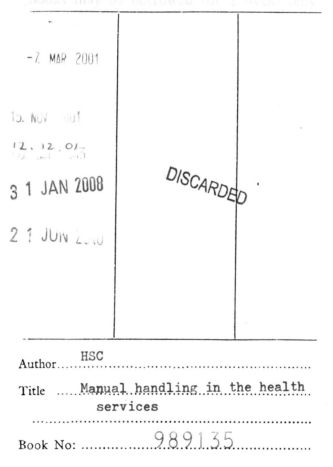
HSE BOOKS

© *Crown copyright 1998*

Applications for reproduction should be made in writing to:

Copyright Unit, Her Majesty's Stationery Office,

St Clements House, 2-16 Colegate, Norwich NR3 1BQ

First published 1992

Reprinted (twice) 1993

Second edition 1998

ISBN 0 7176 1248 1

This is guidance prepared, in consultation with HSE, by the Health Services Advisory Committee which was appointed by the Health and Safety Commission as part of its formal advisory structures. The guidance represents what is considered to be good practice by the members of the Committee. It has been agreed by the Commission. Following this guidance is not compulsory and you are free to take other action. But if you do follow this guidance you will normally be doing enough to comply with the law. Health and safety inspectors seek to secure compliance with the law and may refer to this guidance as illustrating good practice.

Contents

Introduction

1   This book replaces *Guidance on the manual handling of loads in the health service*. It expands and revises the guidance and takes into account the Manual Handling Operations (MHO) Regulations 1992 and other recent legislation.

2   The guidance in this book is intended to help everybody who plays a part in ensuring that risks from manual handling are minimised. It is addressed to senior and line managers responsible for the health and safety of employers and others including patients, contractors and agency staff. It is relevant across the healthcare sector, in hospitals, health centres, nursing homes, general practices, ambulance services and in the community.

3   This guidance demonstrates the benefits of eliminating manual handling where possible, assessing remaining risks and taking steps to reduce them. In keeping with the Manual Handling Operations (MHO) Regulations, it puts forward an approach to risk prevention which involves taking account of the task, the load, the working environment and the individual (the ergonomic approach).

4   Manual handling includes lifting, lowering, pushing, pulling, carrying and supporting loads. This guidance covers patient handling, as well as a wide range of other jobs.

Who should use this guidance?

5   If you are employers or senior managers, such as chief executives and board members, you set the policies and are responsible for ensuring risks are assessed and eliminated or reduced. It is important that you are seen to be actively committed and to support measures to eliminate or minimise risk. If you are senior managers in large organisations, the sections in this guidance on the extent of the problem, the value of safer manual handling, the law, health and safety management, and monitoring are particularly relevant to your role.

6   If you are line managers, such as ward managers and departmental managers, you are responsible for implementing the health and safety policy and procedures. You need to know what these policies and procedures require from you. This guidance will help you make sure that local management systems are adequate, and that there is an upward flow of information to senior managers. Most of the document is relevant to you; some of the sections on special situations may be of particular interest, depending on your responsibilities.

7   Others who can influence policies and practice include back care advisers, trainers, occupational health staff, risk managers and health and safety advisers. Your responsibilities depend on your role. Although this guidance is not directly aimed at you, you should find it helpful when developing your views and advice.

The extent of the problem

8 Nearly a third of all workplace accidents reported to the Health and Safety Executive (HSE) involve manual handling. In the health services that proportion rises to over a half. Between 1992 and 1995 nearly 14 000 manual handling accidents in the health services were reported to HSE, over 60% of them involved patient handling.

9 Manual handling accidents and injuries are not new. Guidance on how to make manual handling less hazardous has been available for years, but the problem has not gone away. Some employers have been successful in tackling manual handling problems through effective management policies, but too many have concentrated on training alone. This has only a limited effect; health and safety law requires more to be done.

10 The best way to tackle manual handling is through an approach based on ergonomics. In essence, ergonomic practice is the practical and scientific study of people in relation to their working environment. An ergonomic approach to manual handling involves looking at the task, the load, the working environment and the individual. Figure 1 shows some of the elements which contribute to safer handling.

Figure 1

The factors which ntribute to safer handling

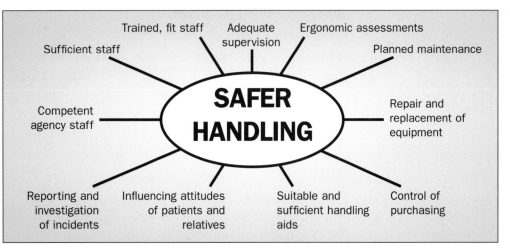

11 Injuries will continue unless manual handling tasks are eliminated, or modified to reduce risk. The costs of injuries are high. About half of all manual handling injuries reported to HSE involve damage to the lower back, and people are often off sick for a long time. They suffer pain, may be unable to lead an active life, and may even be forced to stop work. Recent estimates suggest that every year 3600 nursing staff have to retire because of their injuries; it costs over £30 000 to train a nurse.

12 Sickness absence and the employment of temporary staff are expensive. The loss of skilled staff and compensation claims cost still more. The number of civil actions being brought against employers is rising, as are the sums being awarded. The average award for manual handling injuries is currently £60 000; the largest award to date is £345 000, and at the time of writing one authority is appealing against an award of £435 000. Substantial legal costs are also involved in civil action.

13 During 1995/96 the National Health Service's (NHS's) Permanent Injury Benefit (PIB) Scheme was notified of 1413 new cases of permanent injury of all types; nearly 200 more cases than in the previous year. Six thousand people now receive PIB, which cost £22.4 million in 1995/96; up nearly 20% from the previous year. The cost of Temporary Injury Allowance is believed to run into many millions. An unknown but a large proportion of the injuries under these schemes result from manual handling. The NHS also bears the cost of treating those injured.

14 The following cases illustrate how some of these costs arise.

CASE STUDY 1

Case A

Mrs S, a staff nurse, was instructed by a sister to lift a 102 kg (16 stone) patient with three other nurses using an orthodox lift, while a fifth nurse cleaned and washed the patient and changed the sheets. The patient had severe diarrhoea and had surgery for bilateral knee replacement. Her legs were supported in troughs. The nurses lifted the patient approximately three times, and held her in the air for 30-60 seconds. Mrs S sustained a prolapsed disk. She had two operations and was left with chronic low back pain and a vulnerable back. After this she was fit for only light part-time work. Her civil claim was settled out of court for a total of £57 500.

An expert opinion was obtained that the accident could safely have been avoided by rolling the patient.

Case B

Mrs T was a sister employed in a recovery room. With the assistance of a student nurse, she attempted to lift an extremely heavy patient into position for an X-ray. The Australian lift technique was used, and Mrs T sustained a back injury which caused her to retire from nursing.

Expert opinion indicated that the patient should have been moved on a sliding sheet, or lifted by four nurses. The senior sister had just sent all the other recovery room staff home early because it was near Christmas.

At a hearing the judge decided that, although the employer was negligent because the other staff had been sent home, Mrs T contributed to the accident because she went ahead with the lift instead of waiting for extra help. The judge assessed her blame for the accident at two-thirds, which meant that she recovered £73 023 compensation.

Case C

A patient was wheeled from a dining room to a small toilet cubicle. Two nurses, one of whom was Mrs J, a state enrolled nurse, transferred the patient from the commode and into the toilet cubicle. Mrs J twisted her back while rotating the patient onto the toilet, and sustained a severe injury in her lower back. Mrs J was unable to continue working and was awarded £140 000 compensation.

Case D

Two nurses, one a junior, were using the Australian lift technique to move a patient with multiple sclerosis. The patient suddenly jerked and the junior nurse suffered a severe low back injury. The trial judge decided it was foreseeable that the patient would jerk and awarded damages of £172 000.

Case E

Mrs A, a theatre sister in a private hospital, suffered two lifting and handling accidents in the theatre while lifting patients using canvas and poles. After the first back injury she had a laminectomy. She returned to work without any review of risks or any changes to the procedures, and then suffered a further accident, damaging another part of her spine. She had to retire on the grounds of ill health in her early fifties. She recovered damages of £110 000.

Case F

Ms B was injured while handling a dead patient. The porter who was helping her let go. Ms B suffered serious back injury. She had to retire on health grounds. She received damages of £150 000. Still in her twenties, her lifestyle is restricted and she is in constant pain. She will not work again.

Case G

Mrs J was injured when she was handling a very heavy elderly patient alone. She had not been properly trained. She retired on health grounds, but her employer maintained that she would have retired early in any event. This case was eventually settled for the sum of £82 500. She continues to suffer serious discomfort with her back.

Case H

A physiotherapist sustained a severe back injury using an 'up and down' bed which was faulty because of poor maintenance. The case was settled in court for £117 000.

The value of safer manual handling

15 The experience of one NHS trust shows what can be done through a systematic approach to manual handling. The trust analysed the statistical information available to it and carried out a comprehensive audit of manual handling before taking action. It found that in 1993/94, 6720 hours were lost due to manual handling; 58% of all hours lost due to accidents at work. A 'broad brushstroke' risk assessment showed that there was an urgent need for more equipment and training. Money was found in the capital programme. Approximately £100 000 was spent during the next year, almost exclusively on patient handling equipment. A comprehensive training programme was set up.

16 Analysis following the changes showed an 84% reduction in hours lost because of manual handling accidents, with an estimated saving of £400 000. This result was achieved by close co-operation between the training and development manager, moving and handling co-ordinator, and the health and safety/risk manager.

17 Managers in another trust decided to stop the manual lifting of patients where possible. Risk assessments identified the equipment, furniture and environmental improvements needed to put this policy into practice. They included:

- fabric and rigid sliding aids for moving patients in sitting and lying positions, for example in bed and from bed to trolley or chair;
- hoists to move patients between beds, chairs, commodes, baths, floor, and from a sitting to standing position;
- handling belts to enable staff to help patients into a standing position, and help them walk;
- chairs of various heights with removable arms to help both independent and assisted patient transfers;
- special beds for intensive care wards, and some electric beds in wards;
- increased space - larger toilets, better layouts in bathrooms, and fewer beds in some wards;
- new uniforms, including greater freedom to wear trousers;

- pre-admission information for patients, telling them that equipment might be used to move them;
- arrangements to discuss and assess patient mobility on admission, and to record this information.

18 Targeted training helped staff to change the way they worked, and to use new equipment. As a result of the whole programme, staff reported that they spent more time on the more valuable aspects of their work and felt less physically tired at the end of their shift. Everybody involved saw an improvement in patient and staff care.

Figure 2

Safer manual handling practices reduce accidents to staff and patients alike, reduce costs and improve the quality of care

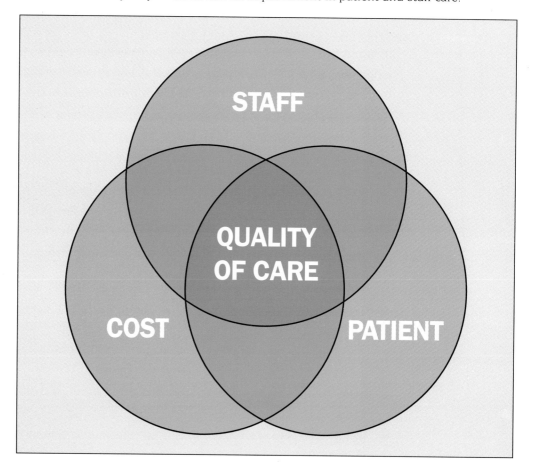

The law

19   The Health and Safety at Work etc Act 1974 (HSW Act) places general duties upon employers, employees and others. The general duties in the Act are developed in the Management of Health and Safety at Work Regulations 1992 (the Management Regulations) and other more specific pieces of law.

20   The Manual Handling Operations (MHO) Regulations 1992 deal specifically with risks from manual handling.

LEGISLATION

Health and Safety at Work etc Act 1974

Employers have to:

- protect the health and safety of their employees;
- protect the health and safety of others who might be affected by the way they go about their work (for example patients being lifted and agency staff);
- prepare a statement of safety policy and the organisation and arrangements for carrying it out (if more than five people are employed);

Employees have to:

- take care of their own health and safety and that of others;
- co-operate with their employer.

Management of Health and Safety at Work Regulations 1992

Employers have to:

- assess health and safety risks to employees and others, to identify the precautions required by health and safety law;
- take particular account in their assessment of risks to new and expectant mothers and their unborn and breast-feeding children;
- make arrangements for planning, organising, controlling, monitoring and reviewing the precautions required by law;
- provide appropriate health surveillance;
- appoint competent people to help them comply with health and safety law;
- provide employees with adequate training and instruction;

- co-operate and co-ordinate with other employers where they share premises or workplaces.

Employees have to:

- use equipment provided by their employers as instructed.

The Approved Code of Practice on the Management of Health and Safety at Work Regulations provides further guidance.[1]

Manual Handling Operations Regulations 1992

Employers have to:

- avoid manual handling operations which involve a risk of injury to employees;
- assess remaining manual handling operations;
- reduce the risk of injury;
- provide general information on the weight of loads;
- review the assessment.

Employees have to:

- make full and proper use of systems of work provided.

The flowchart in Appendix 1 shows the steps to be taken to comply with the Regulations. HSE also publishes general guidance on them.[2,3]

Consultation with employees

21 Two pieces of health and safety law cover consultation with employees. The Safety Representatives and Safety Committees Regulations 1977 deal with consultation of recognised trade unions through their safety representatives. The Health and Safety (Consultation with Employees) Regulations 1996 cover employees who are not covered by trade union safety representatives.

22 More detailed guidance is provided in other HSE publications.[4,5,6] In summary, you must consult employees and their representatives in good time about aspects of their health and safety at work, including:

- any change which may substantially affect their health and safety;
- their employer's arrangements for getting competent health and safety advice;
- the information provided on reducing and dealing with risks;
- the planning of health and safety training;
- the health and safety consequences of introducing new technology.

23 In practice, employers have found that initiatives for reducing manual handling risks are only fully effective if they involve employees and their representatives closely in all aspects, including risk assessment and accident investigation.

Duties to non-employees

24 Under the HSW Act, you have general duties towards people who are not your employees but may be affected by the way you go about your work. These include contractors, students and self-employed people who may work with your staff, or on your premises. Patients and other people who are not at work are also covered.

25 Contracts with staff agencies need to take health and safety into account, so that everybody is clear about who is responsible for what. In some cases you may have the same duties towards agency staff under health and safety law as you do towards your direct employees.

26 People employed by different organisations may share a workplace, or employees of one organisation may work in an area controlled by another. The employers involved need to co-operate and co-ordinate their activities, so that they can all comply with their legal duties.

27 Sometimes the precautions needed to reduce the risk to one group of workers involve changes to another employer's premises. If this is the case, both employers need to discuss the situation and agree what needs to be done.

28 Under the Manual Handling Operations Regulations you only have duties towards your employees. Self-employed people have a duty to look after themselves. But the more general HSW Act duties to non-employees, including patients and contractors, still apply. This means, for example, that you have to consider the risks to patients when they are being moved.

Health and safety management

29 To manage risks from manual handling successfully, you need to show commitment from the top of the organisation. You can express this in a clear statement of policy, which fits within the framework of the overall health and safety policy required by the HSW Act. Key elements of a policy statement include:

■ recognition of the risk;

■ commitment to introducing measures to eliminate or minimise that risk;

■ allocation of responsibilities.

30 Policies need to be supported by more detailed procedures and arrangements covering, for example, working practices, training, incident reporting, and investigation. These will only be effective if everybody knows about them, and if you have arrangements to check how they are working. Many employers have found it helpful to appoint a person or team of people to co-ordinate such programmes.

31 If you are a line manager, you have a crucial role in managing the risks from manual handling. To discharge your role effectively you need proper training, appropriate experience and sufficient authority.

32 Further guidance on managing health and safety is provided in the HSE publication *Management of health and safety in the health services.*[7]

Risk assessment

33 The aim of risk assessment is to identify hazards caused by work activities, the risk that these might cause harm, and the steps needed to control the risk. HSE publishes a useful leaflet entitled *Five steps to risk assessment.*[8] The five steps are:

- decide if there is a problem;
- decide who might be harmed and how;
- evaluate the risks and decide whether existing precautions are adequate or more should be done;
- record your findings;
- review your assessment from time to time and revise it if necessary.

34 If you are an employer, you must carry out risk assessments under the Management Regulations. If these general assessments identify manual handling jobs which involve risks, the first thing you should do is to try to avoid the risk altogether.

35 One way of avoiding risky tasks is to reconsider work patterns. For example, routines which demand that all patients are bathed, washed and dressed by a certain time are now considered inappropriate. Given time and help, many patients may be able to manage for themselves.

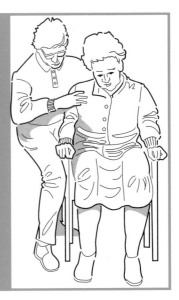

CASE STUDY 2

A surgical ward identified a link between pain and patients' willingness and ability to move post-operatively. Effective pain control measures are now seen as an essential issue in independent movement. As a result, the risks of injury to staff and of post-operative complications due to immobility are reduced; patients are less dependent on nursing staff for mobility needs; staff are available for other tasks and less physically tired; and the quality of patient care has improved.

36   If you cannot eliminate risky jobs, then you must carry out a more detailed assessment. HSE's publication *Manual handling. Manual Handling Operations Regulations* 1992. *Guidance on regulations*[2] contains guidelines to help identify where more detailed assessments might be required. They relate to the handling of objects. Another HSE publication, HSAC's *Getting to grips with handling problems*[9] gives worked examples of assessments in the health services, including tasks involving patient handling.

37   The Manual Handling Operations Regulations deal with the risk of injury to employees involved in handling activities, and do not cover the risks to people or patients being moved. However, unless you include the risks to patients in your manual handling assessments, you will need to make other arrangements for assessing them under the Management Regulations.

38   Carrying out a full assessment of every individual manual handling operation could waste a lot of time and effort. You can group common tasks, such as bed-to-chair or wheelchair-to-toilet transfers, and then carry out a generic assessment. The people doing the work and their managers need to know enough about the risks to judge whether the generic assessment is adequate; if it is not, they need to arrange for an assessment of individual tasks. Local procedures should set out the measures to reduce risk, based on the risk assessments.

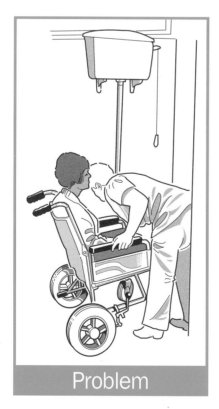

Problem

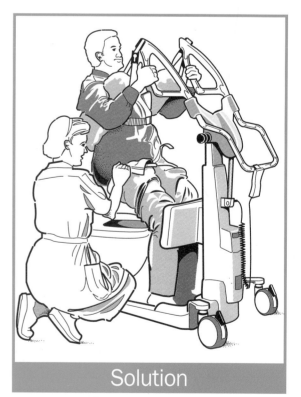

Solution

39 The people who carry out assessments may need training if they are to do the work competently. Depending on how much you expect from them, they may need authority to make decisions or initiate change. They also need enough time to gather information about the tasks and the loads; to discuss this with the people involved; to identify tasks which occur infrequently; to examine the workplace; and to identify suitable mechanical aids. If a number of people are involved in assessment they need to talk to each other and ensure a consistent and co-ordinated approach. In a large organisation it is often useful to appoint an experienced staff member to oversee assessment work.

40 You should ensure that the results of most of the assessments are written down and made available. This does not have to be done if:

■ the assessment is simple, obvious and easy to repeat; or

■ the work is low risk, straightforward, and it will take longer to record the assessment than to do the job.

Assessments must be reviewed if conditions change significantly.

41 When carrying out an assessment, under the Manual Handling Operations Regulations you must consider four main factors:

■ the task;

■ the load (whether an object or a person);

■ the working environment;

■ individual capability.

Assessments need to cover predictable but non-routine situations, such as emergency evacuation of the building and patient falls. In most cases the use of lifting aids will not totally eliminate manual handling, and some assessment will still be needed. While carrying out an assessment, remember risks of injury other than those to the back, for example from sharp edges and extreme temperatures. But above all, remember that assessment is a practical process; it is only as good as identification of good practice or the reduction in risk it produces - it is not an end in itself.

The task

42 You need to ask yourself whether the task involves:

■ holding the load at distance from the trunk;

■ unsatisfactory bodily movement, especially twisting the trunk;

■ poor posture, such as stooping or stretching;

■ excessive movement of the load, especially the distances over which it is lifted or lowered, carried, pushed or pulled;

■ risk of sudden movement of the load;

■ frequent or prolonged physical effort (including maintaining a fixed posture);

■ insufficient rest or recovery periods.

Manual handling operations in a healthcare setting frequently involve one or more of these, and you need to consider the significance of each one.

43 Over-frequent or over-prolonged physical effort over a period of time can make future injury more likely. This needs to be taken into account during the assessment. An aching back or limbs at the end of a working day should not simply be accepted as part of the job. Early warning signs of possible musculoskeletal damage should be identified and appropriate action taken. There are a number of methods which may be used to gauge the postural stresses involved in manual handling. Sources of advice on this are listed in Appendix 3.

CASE STUDY 3

Staff had to wash a variety of basins and containers for several hours a day. Because of the shape and size of the basins, the shallow sink that had previously been used was inadequate. A new, deep, double sink was installed, but soon afterwards staff complained of pains in the shoulders, neck and back.

The local manager spoke to the health and safety adviser, who agreed with the staff that the new sink had not been installed at the right height. Because the sink was too low, staff were constantly reaching below their waist height and working with their arms too far away from their bodies. This was putting strain on different parts of their upper bodies. The health and safety adviser conducted a number of trials so that staff could say what height sink was most comfortable for them. As a result, the sink was raised by about 25 cm. This reduced the risk of injury and the number of staff complaints, increasing staff morale.

Problem

Solution

44 People are more likely to be hurt during manual handling if their job also involves poor postures for other tasks, such as stooping or sitting on badly designed chairs. Poor posture significantly increases the amount of stress on the spine. Some nursing staff may spend up to 30% of their time in a stooped position. You may be able to reduce risks by identifying tasks that involve postural stress (but not necessarily manual handling), and by modifying the task, equipment or workplace to reduce the posture problem.

CASE STUDY 4

Ninety-five percent of patients in a 40-bed facility for young chronic sick were dependent on wheelchairs for mobility. Nursing staff and auxiliaries frequently suffered back injury. To overcome this a strategy was devised to change the emphasis from manual to mechanical handling.

After the purchase of suitable equipment and a period of staff training, there were still many barriers to overcome. At first patients were rather wary of new equipment but, after a period of familiarisation, they accepted the equipment; rather like people used to wearing car seat belts, they eventually felt insecure without it.

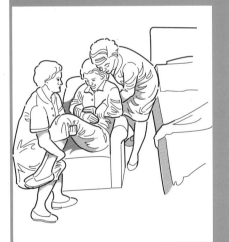

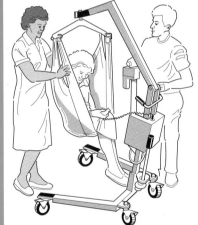

Problem   Solution

Initially using the equipment took slightly longer than the old manual methods, but once both staff and patients were familiarised, the routine movements within the ward could be carried out with some time saving. Once operational, the new arrangements led to virtual elimination of sickness absence related to back problems, with consequent savings. Staff also reported that they felt much less tired at the end of a busy day.

> **CASE STUDY 5**
>
> Staff involved in changing leg ulcer dressings complained of aching backs at the end of a session. Several alterations were made, including the provision of a suitable seat, redesign of the dressing trolley to avoid awkward movement when reaching for dressing supplies, and provision of an adjustable height couch for patients.

45 The number and length of rest or recovery periods is also important. How the work is organised affects the amount of manual handling done by each employee, and the amount done in total. Reorganising the workload to spread manual handling throughout the day allows longer recovery periods. The number of staff available and their skills are also relevant.

The load

46 You need to ask yourself whether the load is:

- heavy;
- bulky or unwieldy;
- difficult to grasp;
- unstable, or with contents likely to shift;
- sharp, hot or otherwise potentially damaging.

These factors are relevant whether the load is an object or a person.

When the load is an object

47 Under the Manual Handling Operations Regulations, you must provide handlers with general indications about the weight of loads and the heaviest side of any load where the centre of gravity is offset. If you can, you should give more precise information. Information can be provided by marking containers; this is especially helpful where employees handle a variety of containers, as are labels which show the contents of loads. Talk to your suppliers about how they can improve labelling and packaging.

48 The shape and size of loads affects how difficult they are to lift; so does the stability of the contents and whether there are any grips or handles. The risk of injury may be reduced by redesigning loads to make them more manageable.

49 When making changes you need to think about any effects they may have, and make sure they do not introduce new hazards. However, solving a problem in one department may lead to benefits elsewhere, while standardising containers makes purchasing, staff training, and storage design easier and cheaper.

CASE STUDY 6

Staff in a hospital had to make up boxes of linen to order. The different items of linen were taken from shelves and loaded into cardboard boxes. The full boxes were loaded on a pallet and moved to an outer storage area. Over 200 linen orders were made up each day. Staff were unhappy with this job because the boxes were large and hard to handle. Some staff with a history of back problems were unable to do it.

The box design, the repeated lifting and stacking, and the fact that staff had no knowledge of what each box weighed put them at risk of back and upper limb injuries. It was decided to make the boxes smaller, lighter and easier to handle. The local manager involved other departments, so that they could bulk-buy the new size boxes. At the same time, a graph giving the weight of each of the standard orders was put on a nearby noticeboard to alert staff to the weight of many of the boxes.

Problem

As a result, the boxes were easier to handle and staff knew more about their weight. This reduced the risk of injuries. The number of complaints from staff reduced, and people could be used more flexibly. Other departments found they could use the new boxes, rather than just store them.

Solution

50 It may be convenient to transport and store goods in bulk, but this can involve risks to employees who have to handle the goods later. Bulk loads may be handled more safely by mechanising the handling operation, or splitting the load into more manageable units at the point of delivery. Remember that mechanisation does not necessarily reduce all manual handling risks, and may even introduce new hazards.

CASE STUDY 7

Medical records staff identified that retrieving and transporting large numbers of patient notes in wire baskets presented a high risk of injury. No existing equipment was found suitable to meet their needs, so they designed a trolley with interlocking pairs of wheeled baskets. This:

■ removed the tripping hazard of baskets on the floor;

■ reduced stooping to load/unload baskets;

■ provided easier access to notes;

■ eliminated the need to lift baskets;

■ resulted in easier transfer of notes to/from clinics.

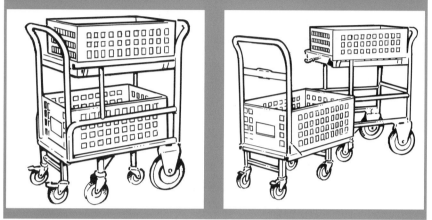

When the load is a person

51   Unlike inanimate loads, people can help (or hinder) the manual handling operation, they may feel pain and anxiety, they have personal dignity and are unique and irreplaceable. Patients may be connected to fragile medical equipment and can become violent or agitated, affecting the way they are handled. They may also have to be placed into or recovered from unusual positions, such as on an X-ray table or theatre table, and the manual handling may be an essential part of their care plan.

CASE STUDY 8

Nursing staff had to help infirm patients by supporting them to the bathroom and helping them in and out of the bath. The patients could be awkward to handle and heavy, presenting a considerable risk of back injury. There was not enough room to use the ward's patient hoist. The bath was against the wall, and nurses could not get on either side to assist patients.

The nursing staff felt there was not enough space to handle the patients. It was difficult for more than one nurse to help, and for them to get into the right position for lifting. The ward sister, in consultation with staff, the health and safety adviser and the moving and handling co-ordinator, proposed changes to the bathroom layout to make handling the patients easier. More space was created by replacing partitions with curtains. The patients kept their privacy but it was easier for staff to manoeuvre them. The bath was moved away from the wall, giving room to use the patient hoist, and staff could get to both sides of the bath.

The changes cost between £2500 and £3000 (up to £6000 today) for each ward, including replacing the flooring, redecorating the area and modifying the toilet to improve access. The risk of back injury was substantially reduced. Increasing the amount of space also allowed two nurses to help the patient, allowed the hoist to be used, and meant patients could manoeuvre themselves more easily.

Problem   Solution

52 Patients who seem to be capable and willing to help at the start of a movement may suddenly find themselves unable to continue. How carers react in these circumstances can affect whether they or patients are injured. You need to think about this sort of situation in advance, and teach the correct response. For example, if a patient stumbles or trips while being helped to walk, the immediate reaction is to try to prevent a fall. Both staff and patients have been injured in such circumstances. If they are properly positioned, it may be safe for carers to allow the patient to slide down their body and onto the floor. They can then make the patient comfortable, decide whether medical attention is needed, and decide whether the patient can get up independently or needs help.

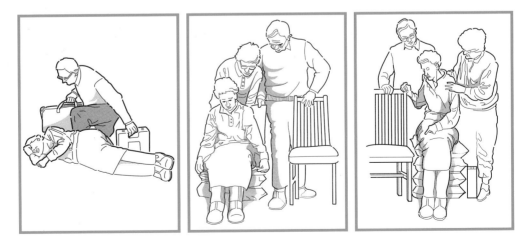

53 It is good practice to include manual handling arrangements in individual care assessments and plans. Whether they are being cared for in a hospital, a nursing or residential home, or in the community, plans which enable patients to do as much as possible for themselves reduce risks to staff and encourage rehabilitation and independence.

54 The care plan or profile needs to be available to all staff who handle the patient and be kept near them. A good plan includes instructions for daytime and night-time care and the following information:

- patient details, including their height and weight. If the precise height and weight is not known, a good estimate may be sufficient;
- the extent of the patient's ability to support his or her own weight and any other relevant factors, for example spasm, fatigue indicators or a tendency to fall;
- problems with comprehension, co-operation or behaviour;
- recommended methods of movement for the relevant tasks such as sitting, going to the toilet, bathing, transfers and movement in bed;
- the minimum number of staff required to help and details of the equipment needed;
- other relevant risk factors such as disability, weakness, pain and skin lesions.

Care plans also need to allow for changes in the condition of patients and their mobility. It is good risk management practice to have a system to record, retrieve and update such plans.

CASE STUDY 9

Case A

The routine procedure for showering a patient in a nursing home involved six separate patient transfers. By assessing the tasks and introducing appropriate changes, the number of patient transfers required was reduced to two.

Originally the patient was first transferred from bed into a wheelchair, then transferred from the wheelchair onto the toilet and then back into the wheelchair again. The patient was then taken to the shower room and transferred onto a shower chair or onto a trolley. After showering, the patient was transferred back into the wheelchair and then finally transferred from the wheelchair back into bed.

By purchasing multi-purpose chairs, which could be used for moving patients from room to room, and positioning patients over the toilet as well as supporting patients in the shower, only two patient transfers were required: from the bed to the new chair and then back into bed.

Case B

In a ward for patients with limited mobility, shower cubicles were originally installed with a tray-type base. Patients had to be helped to step over the base edge. Many patients found this difficult, and because of the restricted space, staff had to put themselves into awkward, risky positions to help. To overcome the problem, shower bases were repositioned so that the upper edge of the base was flush with the surrounding floor.

The working environment

55 You need to ask yourself whether there are:

- space constraints preventing good posture;
- uneven, slippery or unstable floors;
- variations in level of floors or work surfaces;
- extremes of temperature, humidity or air movement;
- poor lighting conditions;
- inadequate or insufficient storage facilities.

56 Space is often at a premium but quite minor alterations can significantly affect the standard of a working environment. Reviewing the layout within wards, bathrooms and other patient areas will help you decide whether there is enough room for manual handling operations to be carried out safely.

CASE STUDY 10

Some older and infirm patients with limited mobility had difficulty getting themselves to the toilet. Hospital staff regularly had to help them, involving a risk of back injury.

The ward sister realised that there was a problem. Limited space made it difficult for staff to adopt good posture, and the sustained effort needed for many heavy patients made this worse. The sister consulted her staff on what could be done.

The toilets already had handles on either side to help the patients position themselves, but they were not within easy reach. Many of the patients were only partially infirm, and improving the handles would allow some of them to support themselves much more. A longer retractable handle was provided to one side of the toilet, so that patients could lift themselves up using both hands. A vertical handle was provided so that patients could hold on to it and pull themselves to their feet.

This allowed many patients to raise themselves with little or no assistance. A number no longer needed help in the toilet, giving greater independence and a sense of achievement. Staff found it much easier to help the others and were pleased with the results. The risk of injury was considerably reduced.

Problem   Solution

57   The design of the working environment is equally important in areas such as offices, kitchens and workshops. The height of workstations such as sinks, shelves, catering and laundry equipment and storage areas is relevant. A workplace may have been designed for a use which has changed over time, or the layout may have been reached in a piecemeal fashion. Both of these situations can cause problems.

CASE STUDY 11

In one hospital toilet facilities were converted to an X-ray film store, with racking to a height of approximately 3 m. Once the racking and films were in place there was not enough room to use steps or any other safe means of access, nor could staff bend down to reach the lower racks without twisting. The designer had found room for the film, but had entirely overlooked the suitability of the workplace that was created.

In contrast, a medical records department elsewhere installed electronically controlled shelving which automatically moved the shelf and relevant records to a comfortable working level. This replaced a traditional storage system, which required step ladders to reach higher shelves, and stooping to reach lower levels.

---

58   Safe manual handling requires floors which are even, non-slip and stable. Floors may become uneven as a result of maintenance work or if coverings are poorly laid or allowed to deteriorate. They may become slippery during routine cleaning, following spillage of liquids or fine powders, or during the course of a work activity. For example, accumulations of wax deposits in histology laboratories can present problems. Carpets may also affect the ease with which staff can move equipment. If manual handling is carried on outdoors, the weather may affect conditions underfoot.

59 Changes in the level of both floors and work surfaces can also increase the risk of injury. While differences in floor levels from one area to another may be difficult to eliminate without major reconstruction, the situation can be improved by the provision of ramps and suitable handrails. This makes it easier to use wheeled equipment, trolleys, wheelchairs and mechanical lifting equipment, and some patients who need help with steps may be able to negotiate a slope. Safe manual handling is easier if unloading bays are designed to be compatible with delivery vehicles.

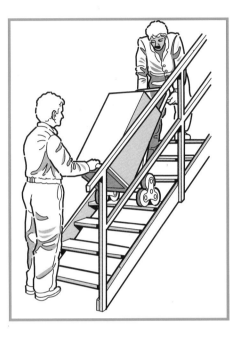

Multi-wheeled trolleys can be used on stairs

60 Extremes of temperature, humidity or air movement may lead to drowsiness, fatigue or loss of sensation, which can affect the way the job is done. There is less risk of injury if manual handling is performed in a comfortable environment.

61 Sufficient well-directed light enables people to see what they are doing clearly and to make accurate judgements of distance and position. Main work areas or thoroughfares must have sufficient and well-maintained lighting, as must stairways, store-rooms and other work areas. Lighting requirements in wards at night may need to be considered as part of a risk assessment.

62 The Workplace (Health, Safety and Welfare) Regulations 1992 cover general requirements for things such as lighting, temperature and the condition of floors. HSE publishes guidance on these requirements in an Approved Code of Practice.[10]

Individual capability

63 You need to ask yourself whether the job:

- requires unusual strength, height or other characteristics;
- puts at risk those who are or were recently pregnant, or who are known to have a history of back trouble, hernia or other health problems;
- requires special knowledge or training if it is to be done safely.

64 The principle behind the Manual Handling Operations Regulations is that the job should be adapted to suit the employee. This means that the physical capabilities of individuals need to be properly assessed, so they are not placed in situations where the job demands too much of them. Any task which can only be done by very strong people needs to be redesigned.

65 Pre-employment health assessment can help to identify those people for whom manual handling tasks present a particular risk. An occupational health adviser can make recommendations on fitness for work, taking into account the relevant risk assessments. Initial assessments of a person's capability will probably not remain valid throughout their period of employment. The assessments should be updated to take account of, for example, injury, ill-health, pregnancy, the natural ageing process or a significant job change. Women who are pregnant or breast-feeding are especially at risk of manual handling injury.

66 Contractors are used throughout the healthcare sector. Their employers, or they themselves if they are self-employed, have the primary duty to comply with any health and safety requirements. But clear arrangements between the contracting parties will help to ensure people are capable and adequately trained to do the work required of them and have the appropriate equipment.

67 Clothing, including protective clothing and uniforms, has a direct impact on ease of movement and posture, for example the traditional straight skirt and fitted bodice of a nurses' uniform does not allow unrestricted movement. Several health service employers are questioning the traditional style of nurses' uniform; a number are experimenting with new designs including culottes and trousers, which are already worn by nursing staff in many other countries. All work clothing and protective equipment should be designed or selected with the job in mind.

68 There is conflicting evidence about the benefits provided by back support belts as an aid to manual handling, indeed in some circumstances they could give the wearer a false sense of security and increase the risk of injury. For these reasons their routine use is not recommended. Employees should not be required to wear them. But if they are worn, then instructions on their use should be given and the effects on staff, beneficial or otherwise, closely monitored.

Reducing risks

69 Risk reduction is a complex matter. There are no quick fixes to solving manual handling problems. The people who do the work may be in a position to influence or modify some risk factors, but many factors will be within the control of the organisation through line managers. Some solutions to manual handling problems become obvious during risk assessment, others require more thought.

70 If you are a line manager, you are responsible for tasks performed by the people who work for you. Active and successful management of the risks from manual handling involves:

- eliminating manual handling operations where possible;
- minimising manual handling operations by reorganising or redesigning the task;
- reducing the risk, for example by providing equipment such as hoists and grab-rails in toilet and bathroom areas, or sack trucks and suitable trolleys in storage areas;
- distributing unavoidable manual handling tasks throughout the working period;
- rotating staff to minimise repetitive or prolonged poor posture and allow for adequate rest and recovery periods;
- providing enough staff who are adequately trained to perform the manual handling tasks safely;
- consulting staff and their representatives on all aspects of manual handling.

71 No employee should be expected to manually handle patients or other loads in circumstances likely to cause themselves or the patient injury. This is one of the factors to be taken into account when deciding on staffing levels, as is the need for adequate supervision.

Equipment

72 The choice of equipment directly affects the way in which manual handling tasks are performed. Variable height work-surfaces, baths, beds, chairs and other equipment can reduce the risk of injury very significantly. When you select a new item of equipment or modify an existing one, you need to consider all aspects of its use to make sure that the needs of both patients and staff will be met. It is sensible to consult users, the manual handling co-ordinator, trainers, the occupational health department and employee representatives before equipment is purchased. Many suppliers can arrange for their equipment to be used by staff for a trial period; this is strongly recommended.

> CASE STUDY 12
>
> In a plastering department, patients had to be lifted on and off a high bench so that the plasterer could apply the cast, creating an obvious risk to staff and patients. The hazard was removed by providing a bench that could be raised and lowered, enabling the patient to get on and off the bench safely, and still allow the plasterer to work at a comfortable height.

73 It is important that equipment is suitable for the user and the task for which it is intended. When selecting or allocating equipment you need to ask yourself:

- Is it suitable for its surroundings?
- Is it manoeuvrable, eg on different floor surfaces and within its intended location, taking account of any restricted access or awkwardly shaped rooms or doorways?
- Is it the right size for the workplace?
- Is it compatible with other equipment and mechanical aids? For example, baths with side panels prevent the proper use of a hoist designed to slide underneath.
- Is it designed to avoid or reduce the need for manual handling?
- Is it adjustable? For example, can the height of a bed be altered to take account of the mobility of the patient, the type of patient transfer to be performed and other equipment; can a bath be lowered for patient access and raised for staff during patient bathing?
- Are self-help grab-rails fixed in appropriate positions in bathrooms, toilets and other areas?
- Is it easy to use, move, adjust and maintain?
- Is it stable in use and fitted with controls and brakes which are effective and easy to use?
- Can mobile equipment be moved safely and without undue effort?
- Is the weight of laden and unladen equipment reasonable?
- Are any adjustable features, such as collapsible arms, foot rests, safety sides, and sectional mattresses, easy to use?

74 You also need to make sure that you have enough equipment available. A shortage of equipment is a common reason for hazardous manual handling tasks being carried out.

CASE STUDY 13

A day surgery unit replaced its patient trolleys and operating table with variable height operating trolleys. Patients appreciated the lower height for easier transfers; staff no longer had to help patients up steps to the trolley; transfers to and from the operating table were eliminated; medical and nursing staff could work at the optimum height.

Manual handling devices

75 Suitable lifting aids are more easily available than they used to be in many workplaces, but they are still often under-used or not used at all. Staff are sometimes reluctant to use aids because they do not know enough about them, distrust the design or maintenance, or believe that patients dislike them. But if manual handling injuries are to be reduced, manual handling itself must be reduced. The selection and use of appropriate lifting aids should therefore be a primary precaution where manual handling cannot be eliminated altogether.

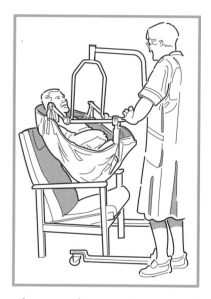

76 This section concentrates on the availability, suitability, safe use and maintenance of such handling aids in general. It does not provide detailed guidance on their use. A number of organisations provide independent advice on selection of such equipment. They include disabled living centres, which offer a wide range of equipment for demonstration, treatment and assessment purposes, and also serve as information resource centres. A list of these centres is given in Appendix 4. Useful information is also contained in the comparative evaluations published by the Medical Devices Agency which are referred to under 'Disability equipment assessments' in the References section.

Availability

77 You need to keep up-to-date with the range of equipment that is available. This can most easily be done by giving the job to someone with enough experience, who can advise you on selection and suitability of items. In many cases the people who carry out manual handling training will be able to do this. However, other staff, such as suitably trained patient care managers or works officers, may be able to keep up-to-date with patient and non-patient lifting equipment. You are more likely to choose the most appropriate equipment if you consult the adviser and users.

78 Equipment needs to be easily available if it is to be properly used. Staff need to know where it is kept, and what it can be used for. One way of doing this is to make line managers responsible for keeping an inventory of lifting equipment used within their area or by their staff. A central inventory of special purpose equipment, which is used less frequently, may help ensure its efficient use.

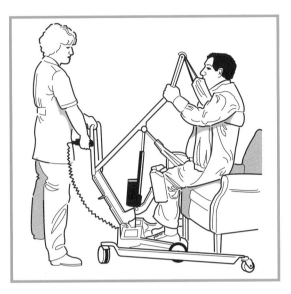

Maintenance

79 Poorly maintained equipment has injured both patients and staff, and created a mistrust of mechanical aids. Under the Provision and Use of Work Equipment Regulations 1992,[11] you must maintain equipment used at work in a safe condition. The type and frequency of maintenance will vary with the type of equipment and its use. Manufacturers' recommendations are relevant when establishing preventive maintenance schedules.

80 People who carry out maintenance or repair work need to understand how the equipment is designed to operate, be able to recognise defects and be able to decide whether they affect continued safe use of the equipment. Such people may be available in-house, or from outside contractors such as the manufacturers. Whether in-house or external staff carry out maintenance, the user is primarily responsible for providing and maintaining safe equipment.

81 You should withdraw from service any equipment you believe to be faulty. Users of equipment are likely to be the first to notice faults. To ensure equipment is put back into service promptly, you need to have an effective internal system for reporting and dealing with faults. In the NHS in England some incidents and accidents involving equipment may be reportable to the Adverse Incident Centre of the Medical Devices Agency. Similar requirements exist in Scotland and Wales.

82 Specific legal requirements cover the construction, examination and testing of some lifting equipment. Legal changes are expected during 1998/99 to implement an Amendment to the Use of Work Equipment Directive. These will introduce specific requirements covering all work equipment used to lift loads, including people.

Training

83 People often think that training in manual lifting techniques is the way to avoid injury. This is not the case; training does not, in itself, successfully solve manual handling problems. Trained people can find themselves trying to apply the techniques in situations where other factors, such as the patient or the environment, are equally important. The provision of training is no guarantee that the skills taught are correctly applied, and training is often focused on professional ward staff, overlooking the needs of other staff groups.

84 Recent evidence suggests that even if all the techniques traditionally recognised as safe are adopted, lifting operations can still cause problems. Lifting with the 'back straight and knees bent' may help to avoid some back problems, but if repeated often enough it can result in cumulative strain in the knee joints. For these reasons, priority should be given to the creation of safe systems of work based on risk assessment. Once this has been done, education and skills training are needed for all relevant staff groups at all levels to complement the total work system. The training and skills of agency and bank staff need to be considered before they start work, and supervisors and managers need to ensure that training is put into practice.

Content and duration of training

85 Several studies indicate that the quality, content and timing of training have often been inadequate in the past. Appropriate training needs to be provided before manual handling tasks are undertaken, and basic training may form part of a general induction programme.

86 Professional trainers have found that a period of three to five days is needed to train healthcare staff who have no previous relevant training or experience in manual handling. But training is an ongoing process, and review or refresher courses need to be planned and implemented.

87 Effective training programmes start with a baseline analysis of the needs of those carrying out manual handling. Professional guidelines may help with this. Programmes tailored to meet the needs of specific occupational groups or working teams are generally the most useful. They enable real situations and tasks to be examined, and make the training more immediately relevant. It is vital to involve all relevant staff, including medical staff where appropriate. As well as ensuring adequate coverage of training, this helps develop a teamwork approach and demonstrate management commitment.

Elements of effective training programmes

Back care – spinal mechanics; the causes of back pain; posture and movements likely to contribute to pain or injury.

Ergonomics – evaluating the environment, task, load and individual capability. How employees can alter their own environment to make work safer.

Mechanical handling equipment – the practical use and care of equipment, its availability and suitability. How to gain the co-operation of patients and reassure them.

Manual handling techniques – basic handling and moving principles so that students can recognise safe approaches and learn to apply them generally, not just in specific situations at work. This will help them to recognise potentially hazardous handling operations.

Fitness – training can usefully emphasise that people need to learn how to use their bodies in all situations: at home; during leisure and at work.

---

88 If you are a manager responsible for work involving manual handling, you may require training so that you can supervise and monitor safe practice, contribute to manual handling assessments, and investigate accidents.

Follow-up training and training records

89 Refresher training at least once a year is essential if training is to remain effective in the long term. You can ensure this through a recall system, covering all relevant staff, including those who are part-time. The nature of the refresher training will depend upon the type of work. Additional training may also be identified as appropriate after injury or incident investigation.

90 You need to record the take up of initial training and follow-up schemes if you want to monitor their value and effectiveness.

Trainers

91 Sufficient expertise is available in many health service organisations to draw together multi-disciplinary teams to provide training across the organisation. Trusts which have used such an approach have found it effective. It means that qualified and experienced staff are able to adapt training to suit local needs and use their experience of solutions developed elsewhere to solve problems. Suitably qualified physiotherapists and occupational health staff are obvious members of training teams, and there are clear benefits in including an ergonomist as a team member. Similarly, design engineers, safety professionals, occupational therapists and nurse tutors, among others, may all have valuable contributions to make.

92 This approach may not be feasible for smaller units. One alternative, successfully applied in a small hospital unit, involves training key personnel. In this instance, ward sisters were trained to deliver practical training to new nursing staff. All manual handling by the new staff member during a specific period was carried out either with the key trainer, or under her direct supervision. Classroom training was delivered shortly after the practical sessions. Similar arrangements could be developed for other staff groups. The success of such an approach may depend on a low staff turnover and a small workforce, it may not, therefore, be generally applicable.

93 Trainers need to be able to teach and assess skills, they may need training in these areas themselves.

Training and information for patients

94 You can encourage patients to help themselves, where they are capable of doing so safely. Staff need enough time to explain the procedure and to allow patients to move at their own pace. Patients may need information and training in the use of equipment. This will reassure them, gain their confidence and help them to co-operate with staff.

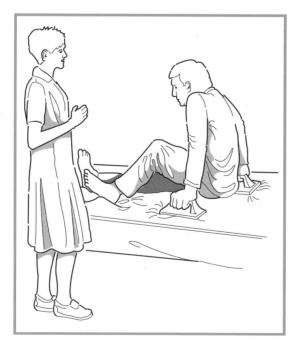

95 Training and information given to patients before operations has been shown to significantly increase their ability to co-operate in moving and handling techniques post-operatively. Such training can usefully include explaining to patients what they are likely to be able to manage after their operation, which moving and handling techniques are likely to be used, and how they can help. Practical demonstrations are particularly useful.

CASE STUDY 14

A gynaecology unit identified that more patients should be encouraged to move themselves pre- and post-operatively. Sliding boards were provided to enable the new systems of patient handling to be implemented, and appropriate staff training provided. Information and demonstrations were included in pre-admission evenings and reinforced on the ward pre-operatively. Patients responded well to this initiative and felt a sense of achievement at being able to move themselves after an operation. They expressed relief at not being so 'dependent'.

Special situations

Ambulance personnel

96 Ambulance crews undertaking routine patient transport and emergency services face particular manual handling problems. They carry out most of their manual handling tasks away from their employer's premises. Crews may be faced with hazards such as stairs, exceptionally heavy patients or violent situations. Nevertheless, a high proportion of the tasks are foreseeable; they must be fully assessed and measures taken to eliminate or minimise risks.

97 You need to make sure that, wherever possible, ambulance personnel are told about manual handling hazards in advance, for example if a patient requires carrying to the ambulance or lives above or below ground floor level. This will help to ensure that the ambulance sent to the job carries the correct manual handling equipment.

98 Ambulance crew must be trained in manual handling techniques and the use of appropriate equipment. They also need to be able to assess risks and make on-the-spot decisions. Comprehensive safe systems of work and procedures for foreseeable events

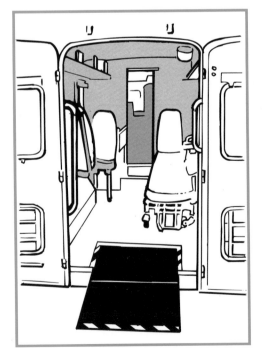
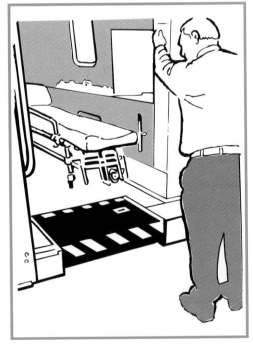

Paramedic ambulance with lowering suspension and retractable ramp *deployed* on the left and *raised* on the right

minimise the need for improvisation. However, in some emergencies ambulance staff may have to work outside established procedures. You need to know about this, so you can learn any lessons and take any action needed. If improvisation is taking place regularly, you need to arrange for further assessment and a re-examination of systems of work.

99 To avoid manual handling by ambulance crews you need to consider the design of ambulances, for example fold-down ramps, hydraulic tail-lifts and rear doors allow safe wheelchair access. Some vehicles have air suspension systems which allow them to settle low, making them easier to load and unload. Fold-down steps and grab-rails help patients with mobility difficulties. Risk assessments will indicate whether modifications are needed to existing equipment, and you need to consider health and safety issues when new vehicles are bought. Careful design and selection of equipment carried on ambulances also eliminates or substantially reduces the need for manual handling.

CASE STUDY 15

Case A

An ambulance trust trialled a neonatal transport incubator on behalf of a number of trusts. The incubator weighted 450 kg and within a month four people sustained back injuries while helping to load it into ambulances. The problem was not helped because ambulances had to visit a number of sites at all times of the day or night, and there were not always suitable staff to help.

The initial assessment suggested:

- the incubator should be redesigned to make it lighter and easier to handle;
- loading bays or ramps should be provided at all trust sites;
- ambulances should have tail-lifts or a lowering suspension system to enable the use of a push-on ramp.

When a new fleet of special ambulances was purchased, they were fitted with lowering suspension and ramps.

Case B

One ambulance trust investigated the manual handling workload of ambulance staff. They looked at the use of fold-down ramps to get wheelchair users in and out of vehicles. They also trialled the use of stretcher trolleys. They found that these arrangements were ineffective at reducing the risk of injury. It was decided that the most effective method would be to fit all ambulances with stretcher tailgates.

100 In cases such as that involving the neonatal transport incubator, or when people are being cared for at home, manual handling risks are shared across several employers. The people involved need to co-operate with one another and co-ordinate their activities so that each one can comply with their legal duties. It may be appropriate for homecare plans to cover what the ambulance service needs to know, including the lifting aids required if they are called out after a fall. Similarly, homecare providers, transportation services and day centres may need to liaise if a client is routinely transported from home to a day centre. Ambulance services and other accident and emergency services also need to work together to minimise manual handling risks.

CASE STUDY 16

An accident and emergency department questioned the frequency with which patients with multiple injuries were being manually handled; the issue was seen as one of patient care as much as staff safety. As a result, special radio-translucent sliding mattresses with handles were provided for each of the trolleys to which these patients were transferred on arrival. This meant that:

■ it was easier to move patients to X-ray and treatment areas;

■ patients appreciated the reduction in physical handling, and thus pain;

■ porters used the mattress as a sliding device to transfer patients from the trolley to the ward bed.

The system of work was complemented with adjustable height trolleys and tables in the X-ray department.

CASE STUDY 17

An ambulance service and hospital trust developed a communication project following complaints about the handling of patients attending outpatient physiotherapy. Discussions identified poor communication between therapists and ambulance personnel as the source of the problem.

Multi-disciplinary training took place in the use of appropriate techniques for transferring and walking the group of patients involved. All chosen techniques were illustrated on laminated sheets carried in the ambulances, along with a standard equipment pack containing transfer belts and boards.

The preferred method of assistance was identified at the patient's initial physiotherapy assessment. The coded information was entered on the ambulance service worksheet, and the patient given a card depicting the chosen manoeuvre.

The improvement in communication greatly enhanced the quality of patient moving and handling.

Caring for people in their homes

101 Many staff perform manual handling tasks away from their employer's premises, including community nurses, occupational therapists, physiotherapists and local authority home care staff. You need to make sure that risk assessments for such work are carried out before staff begin work with a client, and that they take account of the premises, the client's needs and the capabilities of staff assigned to the client. It is important that the different bodies involved work together. As in the hospital setting, health and safety risk assessments can usefully be incorporated into the care plan.

102 In general, community care involves the commissioning of services for a user (client or patient) from a provider. Different providers may be involved in providing the care package for a single user. Providers may come from the health services, social services or an external agency. Under the Management Regulations, all employers who share a workplace must co-operate and co-ordinate their activities so that each can comply with health and safety law.

103 The commissioner and all the various providers need to liaise effectively to ensure that health and safety requirements are met. You will find it easier to get things right from the

start if health and safety is taken into account by the commissioning assessment team before referral, and by the provider who develops the care plan. If you are involved in planning discharge to home or a similar environment, you may need to ensure effective liaison between a number of different groups. Social services staff, the GP, physiotherapist, occupational therapist, community psychiatrist, consultant, hospital and community nursing staff may have an input. Assessments need to be made by competent people and co-ordinated at an appropriate level. A common care plan followed by all agencies caring for a client provides continuity for the client, as well as having health and safety benefits.

CASE STUDY 18

Case A

A disabled patient was discharged to home. Being able to drive, he was able to visit both outpatients for continued treatment, and a day care centre. However, he needed a variety of devices to get from the car seat to the wheelchair. The trust's occupational therapist acted as the care plan co-ordinator and it was decided that a purpose-built hoist, permanently fixed on the car, was the best option. This was successfully installed and meant less risk to staff in the various workplaces, as well as greater freedom for the patient who could now visit more places and friends.

Case B

A rehabilitation unit found that by making the same mobile hoist available on the ward and in the community, carers and elderly patients could be trained in the use of the hoist before they were discharged.

104 Risk assessments and care plans will only be effective if they are based on good background referral information, using real information about the clients, their abilities and their home environment. This requires an open transfer of information; confidential medical and nursing information can be kept elsewhere. Your procedures should allow for any changes in a client's condition to be communicated to all members of the care team and the responses co-ordinated quickly.

105 As elsewhere, risk assessments should identify the precautions needed to reduce risks, including the use of appropriate manual handling equipment. Clients and their carers can get helpful advice from disabled living centres (Appendix 4) and from health or social services' own experts. This may include information on equipment loan, the availability of grants for equipment, and modifications to premises. Even relatively minor modifications, such as non-slip floor coverings or bath seats, can help make manual handling safer for staff and client. Many aids promote client independence, while at the same time, reducing the need for manual handling.

106 Householders cannot be required by health and safety law to adapt their home or provide equipment to reduce risks to visiting nurses or care staff. However, with their co-operation, much can be done to eliminate or reduce the need for manual handling.

Forward planning helps ensure that equipment is available, adaptations are made to the home and all involved are trained in handling techniques. For example, both patient and carer can be trained, before discharge, to use a sliding board to move from a bed to a chair in hospital. Risk assessments may be required for the issue and delivery of equipment.

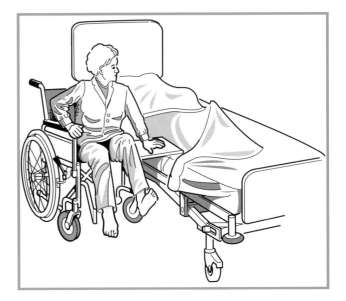

107 While the service user or client has no duty under health and safety law to co-operate with the provider, employers still have duties to their staff when working in clients' homes. If a client refuses to co-operate over the purchase or use of equipment, equipment maintenance, arrangement of furniture or other safety aspects of the home environment, you may need to restrict the duties of caring staff to ensure their safety.

108 Some employers already take a systematic approach where patients or their families resist the use of hoists or other devices. In one case this involves the line manager visiting to explain the purpose of the equipment in avoiding injury to the patient and employee. The manager also explains that continued refusal would result in the withdrawal of the aspect of care that involves lifting. For example, in a case where a householder refused to allow a hoist to be fitted to enable safe use of the bath, the patient was given bed baths instead.

CASE STUDY 19

An 83-year-old patient weighing 83 kg (13 stone) was discharged from hospital at her family's request, although she was still mentally confused. A bed with safety sides was supplied but it was rejected by the family because it was too high for the patient. Two community nurses attended the patient and found her behaviour unpredictable and aggressive. On one occasion while they were helping her out of the bed the patient lifted both her feet, placing her full weight on the nurses, who had to lower her to the floor. Both nurses experienced back pain. The strain of providing two nurses for each visit over a long period was considered to be unacceptable and three alternatives were considered:

- provision of a hoist - this was thought to be unsafe because the patient was unco-operative and likely to thrash about;

- re-admission to hospital - this was strongly opposed by the family;

- provision of a bed whose height could be adjusted.

This last alternative was adopted and, after some delay in obtaining an appropriate bed, the problem was resolved.

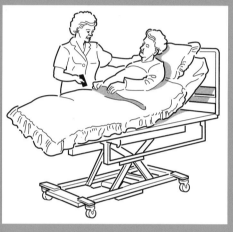

109 Staff training needs to cover all manual handling situations likely in the community, with staff warned of particular hazards and the precautions to be taken. They will probably need to be trained to make on-the-spot evaluations, and need to be told who to contact for advice on specific manual handling problems.

110 Community staff often work alone, and may be at risk of injury because of this. Your risk assessments may need to consider staffing levels; more than one staff member may be required to carry out certain manual handling tasks for some clients.

111 When working alone in the client's home, staff may find it difficult to refuse to undertake certain activities which put their safety at risk. Training can help them to respond appropriately.

Mobile blood transfusion services

112 Blood transfusion sessions are often held in places which are not controlled by the healthcare employer. If you are involved in selecting or approving places for transfusion sessions, remember to consider manual handling hazards. For example, steps, slippery floors and heavy furniture which needs to be moved all increase the risk. Parking arrangements, access to buildings and the distance equipment has to be moved are also relevant. You also need to pay attention to space and layout. Risks for those working with donors are reduced if they can sit with their knees under the beds, with equipment at a level where everything is to hand without twisting or bending.

113 Careful selection of equipment and furniture used in transport and for the sessions helps minimise risks. For example, beds which are of adjustable height, lightweight and have hand grips are easier to use and transport. It also helps if boxes for carrying items are not bulky, but lightweight and have handles. Vehicles can be fitted with hydraulic tail-lifts, equipment can be transported on and off vehicles in suitable cages, lifting trolleys can be provided and portable ramps can be used to overcome steps.

114 Many sites are used regularly for donor sessions. Close liaison between the owner and the Blood Transfusion Service helps ensure that any health and safety hazards are put right, any modifications which are needed are made and the room is laid out as required before sessions.

Maternity units

115 When carrying out risk assessments, remember risks to staff helping at birth and afterwards.

116 Women are being offered greater choice in how they give birth. However, it is important that the health and safety of staff is taken into account when planning these options. This can be considered when the birth plan is agreed. If attention is not paid to design of equipment and working environment, some of the options may involve staff maintaining static postures for long periods. Good design of birthing pools can minimise the strain on staff musculoskeletal systems. For example, the sides of the pool can be concave, to accommodate knees. The pool could also have a built-in seat for the mother to sit on, which can be used for examinations and delivery.

117 Staff who help mothers with breast-feeding can find themselves adopting poor postures for a long time. It might help to re-examine the techniques being used and ensure chairs provide sufficient support.

Maintaining mobility and rehabilitation of patients

118 The aim of manual handling policies is to eliminate hazardous lifting and handling, and to decrease the risks of injury to staff by the use of appropriate equipment. However, there are limited circumstances where staff work at higher risk as part of a specified care or treatment process. The risks involved may include those associated with poor posture, as well as manual handling.

119 One place where this occurs is in the rehabilitation setting. Several groups of care workers (particularly physiotherapists and occupational therapists and their assistants) need to include physical handling as part of the treatment given. The techniques they use should complement the use of equipment such as standing and walking aids, rather than act as an alternative method of treatment.

120 If you are a manager responsible for such work, you should ensure that patient rehabilitation programmes minimise the risk to staff or carers as far as possible. Your manual handling policies need to acknowledge and address these situations, identifying the groups of staff involved, the settings in which they are working, the training provision and treatment techniques. These should be considered as part of risk assessment. Appropriate control measures may include better rehabilitation equipment, increased levels of staffing and specific training.

Working with babies and small children

121 Care staff working with babies and small children also need to be covered by manual handling risk assessments. Careful selection of nursery equipment and furniture helps to avoid manual handling and postural problems. Staff training needs to be tailored to the job and cover, for example, dealing with struggling children. Even small children with disabilities or learning difficulties can present handling problems due to stiffness, weakness and the presence of splints and braces. Handling of those sitting in intimately moulded seating is easier if they are hoisted from their chairs, with a sling left behind them.

Heavy patients

122 Some patients are much heavier than others. A very heavy child of 120 kg (10 stone) could present as many problems as a very heavy adult of 306 kg (26 stone). Manual handling assessments have to recognise this; standard protocols and equipment may not be able to cope with a very heavy patient.

123 You need to make sure that arrangements are in place to identify such patients before they arrive on the ward, so that a comprehensive risk assessment can be carried out, covering all relevant staff groups such as radiographers, porters and technicians. Special equipment may be needed for handling very heavy patients, both in a hospital

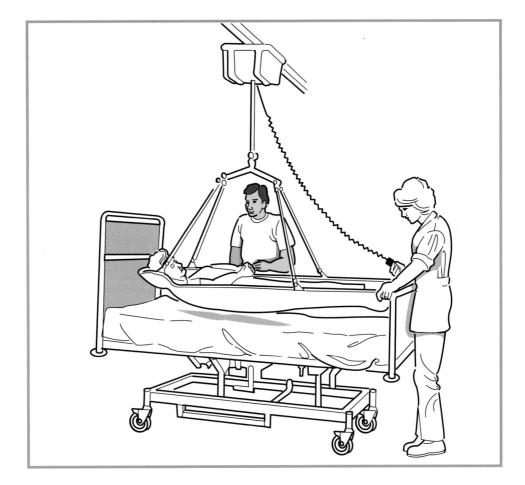

and the community. Power-operated beds, powered hoists, as well as specially adapted commodes, wheelchairs and walking frames, are all available. Finally, the assessment also needs to consider what should be done if a patient collapses or dies.

CASE STUDY 20

A patient weighing over 300 kg (25 stone) was admitted to hospital following an emergency call. The fire brigade moved her from her house into the ambulance and carried out all subsequent manual lifting at the hospital until the patient's death three days later.

The difficulties which the trust found in caring for the patient included:

- the beds and lifting equipment could not accommodate patients over 300 kg (25 stone);
- the bed was unstable except at its lowest level, and there was insufficient room to safely move and position the patient;
- it was either extremely difficult or impossible to carry out investigations, treatments and nursing care or procedures, such as X-rays, catheterisation,

resuscitation and basic nursing care;

- it was impossible to change the bed linen or to sit the patient up in bed;

- the patient's body had to be transferred to the mortuary on the bed, involving the closure of the main corridor;

- the mortuary store was too small to accommodate the body and so it remained on one of the two post-mortem tables for three days;

- the body was eventually removed by the efforts of 12 fire brigade personnel, an electric tug and a vehicle with a crane attached.

The divisional fire officer later stated that while emergency assistance will always be given to getting a sick patient to hospital, they would not help with 'routine' handling in future.

The trust subsequently initiated an 'extremely heavy patient' protocol. This covered the availability of adequate equipment and safe handling procedures for all foreseeable circumstances, including patient falls and death.

Monitoring

124 To assess the effectiveness of your arrangements for reducing risk, you need to systematically monitor what is happening in practice. Measures which are not working, or which have unforeseen consequences, can then be changed. Active monitoring involves checking that systems and procedures are working without waiting until something goes wrong. Appendix 2 provides a checklist which may help line managers examine arrangements in their area of responsibility.

125 Accident and injury data also provide information on the effectiveness of precautions, and helps everyone learn from experience. But if you introduce new measures you may not find that the number of reports goes down in the short term. Reviews of manual handling programmes have often found that reports of back pain and injury increase with staff awareness. This is not necessarily a bad thing; it indicates how much the original problem was underestimated, and ought to generate greater confidence in ill-health and accident data.

Investigation of accidents and incidents

126 Certain accidents are reportable to HSE under the Reporting of Injuries, Diseases and Dangerous Occurrences Regulations 1995;[12] records must be kept of these. Effective health and safety management systems ensure the internal reporting, recording and investigation of a wider range of accidents and incidents than those which are legally reportable. It helps if schemes for internal reporting and recording of manual handling injuries pick up the effects of cumulative stresses, so far as is possible. Staff can be actively encouraged to inform their manager and seek occupational health advice for cumulative strains or pains, as well as discrete incidents.

127 The analysis and investigation of manual handling incidents, whether reportable or not, help to identify causes, trends, the level of compliance with the law, the effectiveness of the precautions, and problem areas.

128 The depth of each investigation will vary, depending on the nature of the incident. To be worthwhile, however, any investigation needs to consider the underlying causes carefully. For example, an investigation which finds that a porter suffered a back injury because a bed moved while he was lifting a patient onto it should identify why the bed moved. The cause may have been that wheel locks were not fitted, not properly applied, or faulty; or the injury may be attributable to another cause altogether. Action after an accident will not be effective if it only addresses the superficial and obvious causes, and misses more significant issues.

CASE STUDY 21

An investigation report stated that a person was burnt by fat while lifting a tray of hot turkeys in a kitchen. This report failed to identify that the person was unable to hold the tray steady because of its weight and its distance from their trunk. As well as burns, he had felt back pain.

129 The format of investigation reports and the management level at which investigations are carried out will depend upon the size and structure of each organisation. However, all investigation reports should aim to provide information to enable decisions about future action. Senior managers also require information on issues such as the overall costs of manual handling accidents. The involvement of the trainer and occupational health and safety staff in investigations helps ensure that the correct future action is taken to prevent recurrence.

130 Remember that social security law[13,14] requires employers to keep an accident book or something similar which is accessible to staff.

Health surveillance and rehabilitation for staff

131 Research suggests that the manner in which an employer responds to an injured employee can have a significant effect on their recovery and return to work. If you take an active interest in the rehabilitation of staff injured at work you send a clear message to the injured person that they are needed and valued. Prompt assessment and treatment of back pain may also add to the effectiveness of treatment.

132 It is useful if employees injured as a result of manual handling, including those suffering cumulative effects, are offered early assessment by the occupational health department. It is good practice to:

- plan a rehabilitation programme which meets the individual's needs;
- monitor the rehabilitation programme through occupational health staff and the line manager;
- reinforce the principles of safe handling and, where relevant, back care;
- review the circumstances and environment in which the injury occurred, and revise the risk assessment if necessary;
- arrange for an occupational health physician to carry out a final assessment of the individual's capabilities before return to full duties.

133 Employees who experience back pain or other symptoms associated with manual handling should be encouraged to go to their occupational health service for an assessment.

References

1 *Management of health and safety at work. Management of Health and Safety at Work Regulations 1992. Approved Code of Practice* L21 HSE Books 1992 ISBN 0 7176 0412 8

2 *Manual handling. Manual Handling Operations Regulations 1992. Guidance on regulations* L23 HSE Books 1992 ISBN 0 7176 0411 X

3 *Getting to grips with manual handling. A short guide for employers* INDG143 HSE Books 1993 Single copies available free, multiple copies in priced packs ISBN 0 7176 0966 9

4 *Safety representatives and safety committees* (The Brown Book) Third edition. Approved Code of Practice and guidance on regulations L87 HSE Books 1996 0 7176 12201

5 *A guide to the Health and Safety (Consultation with Employees) Regulations 1996* L95 HSE Books 1996 ISBN 0 7176 1234 1

6 *Consulting employees on health and safety - a guide to the law* INDG232 Free leaflet HSE Books 1996

7 *Management of health and safety in the health services - information for directors and managers* HSE Books 1994 ISBN 0 7176 08441

8 *Five steps to risk assessment* INDG163 HSE Books 1995 Single copies available free, multiple copies in priced packs ISBN 0 7176 0904 9

9 *Getting to grips with handling problems. Worked examples of assessment and reduction of risk in the health services* HSE Books 1994 ISBN 0 7176 0622 8

10 *Workplace health, safety and welfare. Workplace (Health, Safety and Welfare) Regulations 1992. Approved Code of Practice and guidance* HSE Books 1992 ISBN 0 7176 0413 6

11 *Work equipment. Provision and Use of Work Equipment Regulations 1992. Guidance on regulations* HSE Books 1992 ISBN 0 7176 0414 4 (Due to be revised later in 1998)

12 *A guide to the Reporting of Injuries, Diseases and Dangerous Occurrences Regulations 1995* L73 HSE Books 1996 ISBN 0 7176 1012 8

13 *The Social Security Act 1975* Chapter 14 HMSO 1979 ISBN 10 5414 751

14 *The Social Security (Claims and Payments) Regulations* 1977 SI 977/500 HMSO 1977 ISBN 0 11 093628 0

Suggestions for further reading

The following publications may be of interest, they are all available from HSE Books:

Articles and Substances Used at Work (HSW Act 1974): the legal duties of designers, manufacturers, importers and suppliers, and erectors and installers INDG1 HSE Books 1991

If the task fits. Ergonomics at work INDG90 HSE Books 1991

Management of occupational health services for healthcare staff HSE Books 1993 ISBN 0 11 882127 X

New and expectant mothers at work: A guide for employees HSG122 HSE Books 1994 ISBN 0 7176 0826 3

Disability equipment assessments

The Medical Devices Agency publishes the following disability equipment assessments:

No A3 - Domestic Mobile Hoists

No A19 - Moving and Transferring Equipment

No A23 - Handling Equipment for Moving Dependent People in Bed

These may be obtained from Medical Devices Agency, Hannibal House, Elephant and Castle, London SE1 6TQ

Other useful addresses

A number of trade unions, professional bodies and charities also publish relevant material. They include:

UNISON, UNISON Communications, 20 Grand Depot Road, London SE18

Royal College of Nursing, 20 Cavendish Square, London W1M OAB

The Chartered Society of Physiotherapy, 14 Bedford Row, London WC1R 4ED

National Back Exchange, 8 Trafford Close, Shenley, Herts WD7 9HU

Disabled Living Centres Council, First Floor, Winchester House, 11 Cranmer Road, London SW9 6EJ

National Back Pain Association, 16 Elmtree Road, Teddington, MIDDX, TW11 8ST

Appendix 1
MHO Regulations – flowchart

The Manual Handling Operations Regulations

Regulation 2(1)

| Do the Regulations apply, ie does the work involve manual handling operations? | **No** → |

↓ **Yes**

Regulation 4(1)(a)

| Is there a risk of injury? | **No** → |

↓ **Yes/possibly**

| Is it reasonably practicable to avoid moving the load? | **Yes** → |

↓ **No**

| Is it reasonably practicable to automate or mechanise the operations? | **Yes** → |

↓ **No**

Regulation 4(1)(b)(i)

| Does some risk of manual handling injury remain? | **No** → |

| Carry out manual handling assessment | **Yes/possibly** ↑ |

↓

Regulation 4(1)(b)(ii)

| Determine measures to reduce risk of injury to the lowest level reasonably practicable |

↓

| Implement the measures |

↓

| Is risk of injury sufficiently reduced? | **Yes** → |

No ←

↓ **No**

Regulation 4(2)

| End of initial exercise |

↓

| Review if conditions change significantly |

Appendix 2
Management checklist

❏ Is there a manual handling policy which recognises the risk, makes a commitment to introduce measures to reduce the risk, and allocates responsibilities?

❏ Is the policy supported by more detailed procedures?

❏ Has a manual handling programme been implemented and a person or team of people been appointed to co-ordinate it?

❏ Have risk assessments under the Management Regulations, and where necessary under the Manual Handling Operations Regulations, been carried out?

❏ Are the assessors competent and do they have the necessary expertise?

❏ Unless the assessment was simple and obvious, are the results written down and available?

❏ Do the assessments cover predictable but non-routine situations, eg evacuations or patient falls?

❏ Do the assessments cover the load, the working environment and individual capacity?

The task

Do the assessments consider whether the task involves:

❏ holding the load at a distance from the trunk?

❏ unsatisfactory bodily movement or posture, especially twisting the trunk, or poor posture such as stooping or stretching?

❏ excessive movement of the load, especially the distances over which it is lifted or lowered, carried, pushed or pulled?

❏ risk of sudden movement of the load?

❏ frequent or prolonged physical effort (including maintaining a fixed posture)?

❏ insufficient rest or recovery periods?

The load

Do the assessments consider whether the load is:

❏ heavy?

❏ bulky or unwieldy?

❏ difficult to grasp?

❏ unstable, or with contents likely to shift?

❏ sharp, hot or otherwise potentially damaging?

When the load is a person, are manual handling arrangements set out in each patient's case assessment and case plan?

Are patients encouraged to help themselves?

The working environment

Do the assessments consider:

❏ space constraints preventing good posture?

❏ uneven, slippery or unstable floors?

❏ variations in level of floors or work surfaces?

❏ extremes of temperature, humidity or air movement?

❏ poor lighting conditions?

❏ inadequate or insufficient storage facilities'?

Individual capability

Do the assessments consider whether the jobs:

❏ require unusual strength, height etc?

❏ put at risk those who are or were recently pregnant, or who are known to have a history of back trouble, hernia or other health problems?

❏ require special knowledge or training if they are to be done safely?

Risk reduction

Have the following steps been taken to reduce risks:

❑ elimination of manual handling operations where possible?

❑ minimisation of manual handling operations by reorganising or redesigning the task?

❑ reduction of the risk, for example by providing equipment such as hoists and grab-rails in toilet and bathroom areas?

❑ distribution of unavoidable manual handling tasks throughout the working period?

❑ rotation of staff to minimise repetitive or prolonged poor posture and allow for adequate rest and recovery periods?

❑ provision of sufficient staff adequately trained to perform the manual handling tasks safely?

Equipment

Is there a system in place to ensure that equipment is:

❑ suitable for its surroundings?

❑ compatible with other equipment and mechanical aids?

❑ designed to avoid or reduce the need for manual handling?

❑ easy to move, adjust and maintain?

Manual handling devices

❑ Are sufficient lifting aids available?

❑ Are they used?

❑ Are they maintained?

Training

❑ Has appropriate training been given to all staff, including medical staff, before manual handling tasks are undertaken? Have you been trained so that you can supervise, monitor, contribute to assessments and investigate accidents?

❏ Is there a programme of follow-up training?

❏ Are training records kept?

Monitoring

❏ Do you have a system to monitor what is happening?

Investigation of accidents and incidents

❏ Is there a system for internal reporting, recording and investigation of incidents?

❏ Do investigations identify underlying causes?

❏ Is action taken to prevent further recurrences?

Health surveillance and rehabilitation for staff

❏ Where needed, are arrangements made for suitable rehabilitation programmes tailored to the individual?

❏ Are rehabilitation programmes monitored by occupational health staff and the line manager?

❏ Is there a system for reinforcing the principles of safe handling and, where relevant, back care?

❏ Is there a system for reviewing the circumstances and environment in which the injury occurred, and reassessing the risk if necessary?

❏ Are there arrangements for final assessment by the occupational health physician before people return to full duties?

❏ Are staff who experience back pain or other symptoms associated with manual handling encouraged to go to their occupational health service?

Sources of advice on postural stress

Wilson J R and Corlett E N (eds) *Evaluation of human work: A practical ergonomics methodology* Chapter 23 Corlett E N 'The evaluation of posture and its effects' (second edition) Taylor and Francis 1995.

This has full information on OWAS (Ovako Working Posture Analysing System), RULA (Rapid Upper Limb Assessment), Body Part Discomfort Survey, Nordic Questionnaire (HSE version), as well as information on CODA (Cartesian Optoelectronic Dynamic Anthropometer) and Posture Targeting and references to other tools.

REBA (Rapid Entire Body Assessment)
(copyright) Lynn McAtamney and Sue Hignett

This is a rapid analysis tool for risk rating the posture, activity, coupling and forces related to perform a given task. It is a software package intended to be used as part of a wider ergonomics evaluation.

Contact: Dr Lynn McAtamney
25 Ashchurch Drive
Wollaton
Nottingham NG8 2RB
E-mail cope@dial.pipex.com

Appendix 4

Disabled living centres

ABERDEEN

Hillylands Disabled Living Centre, Croft Road, Mastrick, ABERDEEN, Scotland AB2 6RB
Tel: 01224 685247   Fax: 01224 663144

AYLESBURY

Independent Living Exhibition, Stoke Mandeville Hospital, Mandeville Road,
AYLESBURY, Bucks HP21 8AL
Tel: 01296 315066

BECKENHAM

BATH, Lewis House, 30 Beckenham Road, BECKENHAM, Kent BR3 4LS
Tel: 0181 663 3345

BELFAST

The Disabled Living Centre, Regional Disablement Services, Musgrave Park Hospital,
Stockman's Lane, BELFAST, Northern Ireland BT9 7JB
Tel: 01232 669501 x 2708   Fax: 01232 683662

BIRMINGHAM

The Disabled Living Centre, 260 Broad Street, BIRMINGHAM B1 2HF
Tel: 0121 643 0980

BRISTOL

The Disabled Living Centre, The Vassall Centre, Gill Avenue, Fishponds, BRISTOL
Tel: 0117 965 3651   Fax: 0117 965 3652

CARDIFF

Disabled Living Centre, Rookwood Hospital, Fairwater Road, Llandaff, CARDIFF,
South Glamorgan CF5 2YN
Tel: 01222 566281 x 3751/3787   Fax: 01222 578509

CARMARTHEN

CWM Disability Centre for Independent Living, Coomb Cheshire Home, Langynog,
CARMARTHEN, Dyfed, Wales SA33 5HP
Tel: 01267 241743   Fax: 01267 241874

COLCHESTER

Disabled Living Centre, Occupational Therapy Department, Colchester General Hospital, Turner Road, COLCHESTER, Essex CO4 5JL

Tel: 01206 832172/832173

DUNSTABLE

The Disability Resource Centre, Poynters House, Poynters Road, DUNSTABLE LU5 7TP

Tel: 01582 470900

EDINBURGH

Lothian Disabled Living Centre, Astley Ainslie Hospital, Grange Loan, EDINBURGH EH9 2HL

Tel: 0131 537 9190

ELGIN

Moray Resource Centre, Maisondieu Road, ELGIN, Morayshire IV30 1RX

Tel: 01343 551339 Fax: 01343 542014

EXETER

Independent Living Centre, St Loye's School of Occupational Therapy, Millbrook House, Millbrook Lane, Topsham Road, EXETER, Devon EX2 6ES

Tel: 01392 59260

GRANGEMOUTH

Dundas Resource Centre, Oxgang Road, GRANGEMOUTH KF3 0EF

Tel: 01324 665546

HUDDERSFIELD

Level Best, Access Point, Zetland Street, HUDDERSFIELD, West Yorks HD1 2RA

Tel: 01484 453000 Fax: 01484 542232

HULL

National Demonstration Centre, St Hilda House, Kingston General Hospital, Beverley Road, HULL HU3 1UR

Tel: 01482 225034 Fax: 01482 589002

INVERNESS

Disabled Living Centre, Occupational Therapy Department, Raigmore Hospital, Old Perth Road, INVERNESS, Scotland

Tel: 01463 704000 x 5477

LEEDS

The William Merritt Department, St Mary's Hospital, Greenhill Road, Armley, LEEDS W. Yorks LS12 3QE

Tel: 0113 279 3140 Fax: 0133 231 9291

LEICESTER

The Leicester Disabled Living Centre, Disabled Living Centre, British Red Cross Medical
Aid, 76 Clareden Park Road, LEICESTER, Leicestershire LE2 3AD
Tel: 0116 270 0515 Fax: 0116 244 8625

LEWES

East Sussex Disability Living Centre, 47 Western Road, LEWES, East Sussex BN7 1RL
Tel: 01273 472860

LIVERPOOL

Liverpool Disabled Living Centre, 101-103 Kempton Street, LIVERPOOL, Merseyside L3 8HE
Tel: 0151 298 2055 Fax: 0151 298 2952

LONDON

The Disabled Living Foundation, Equipment Centre and Information Service,
380-384 Harrow Road, LONDON W9 2HU
Tel: 0171 289 6111 Fax: 0171 266 2922

LOWESTOFT

Waveney Centre for Independent Living, 161 Rotterdam Road, LOWESTOFT,
Suffolk NR32 2EZ
Tel: 01502 405454

MACCLESFIELD

Disabled Living Centre, West Park Branch, Macclesfield District General Hospital,
Victoria Road, MACCLESFIELD, Cheshire SK10 2BL
Tel: 01625 661740 (c/o Wheelchair services)

MANCHESTER

Regional Disabled Living Centre, Disabled Living Centre, Redbank House,
4 St Chad's Street, MANCHESTER, M8 8QA
Tel: 0161 832 3678 Fax: 0161 835 3591

MIDDLESBROUGH

Independent Living Centre, Occupational Therapy Dept, Middlesbrough General Hospital,
Ayresome Green Lane, MIDDLESBROUGH, Cleveland TS5 5AZ
Tel: 01642 827471

NEWCASTLE-UNDER-LYME

The Independent Living Centre, The Pitfield Centre, The Brampton,
NEWCASTLE-UNDER-LYME, Staffs ST5 0PQ
Tel: 01782 634949

NOTTINGHAM

Disabilities Living Centre (Nottingham), Lenton Business Centre, Lenton Boulevard, NOTTINGHAM NG7 2BY

Tel: 0115 942 0391   Fax: 0115 9420391

OXFORD

Disability (Count Disability Information Resource), Rivermead Centre, Abingdon Road, OXFORD, Oxon OX1 4XD

Tel: 01865 798723   Fax: 01865 798723

PAISLEY

Disability Centre for Independent Living, Community Services Centre, Queen Street, PAISLEY, Strathclyde PA1 2TU

Tel: 0141 887 0597

PAPWORTH

Papworth Disability Resource Centre, Ermine Street North, PAPWORTH EVERARD, Cambridgeshire CB3 8RH

Tel: 01480 830495

PORTSMOUTH

The Frank Sorrell Dial Disability Centre, Prince Albert Road, Eastney, PORTSMOUTH, Hants PO4 9HR

Tel: 01705 737174   Fax: 01705 821770

SEMINGTON

West Wiltshire & Bath Independent Living Centre, St George's, SEMINGTON, Wilts BA14 6JQ

Tel: 01380 871007   Fax: 01380 871113

SHREWSBURY

Shropshire Disability Resource Centre, Lancaster Road, Harlescott, SHREWSBURY, Shropshire SY1 3NJ

Tel: 01743 444599   Fax: 01743 461349

SOUTHAMPTON

Southampton Aid and Equipment Centre, Southampton General Hospital, Tremona Road, SOUTHAMPTON SO16 6YD

Tel: 01703 796631   Fax: 01703 694756

ST ANDREWS

St David's Centre, Disabled Living Centre, Albany Park, ST ANDREWS, Fife KY16 8DB

Tel: 01334 412606

62

STAMFORD

Disability Living Centre (Lincolnshire), 33 Ryhall Road, STAMFORD, Lincolnshire PE9 1UF

Tel: 01703 480599 Fax: 01703 794756

STOCKPORT

Independent Living Centre, St Thomas' Hospital, Shaw Heath, STOCKPORT, Cheshire SK3 8BL

Tel: 0161 419 4476

SWANSEA

Disabled Living Assessment Centre, St John's Road, Manselton, SWANSEA, Wales SA5 8PR

Tel: 01792 580161 Fax: 01792 585682

SWINDON

Options Plus, Marshgate, Stratton Road, SWINDON, Wilts SN1 2PN

Tel: 01793 643966

UXBRIDGE

Hillingdon Independent Living Centre, Colham Road, UXBRIDGE, Middlesex UB8 3UR

Tel: 01895 233691 Fax: 01895 813843

WELWYN GARDEN CITY

Herts Association for the Disabled, The Woodside Centre, The Commons,
WELWYN GARDEN CITY, Herts AL7 4DD

Tel: 01707 324581 Fax: 01707 371297

64

Printed and published by the Health and Safety Executive   C100   3/98